Disney's Year Book 1992

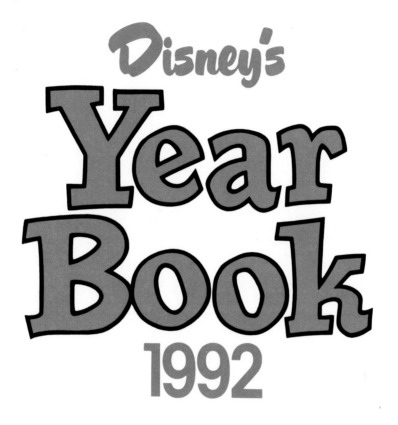

Disney's Year Book 1992

GROLIER ENTERPRISES INC.
Danbury, Connecticut

FERN L. MAMBERG   *Executive Editor*
MICHÈLE A. MCLEAN   *Art Director*
HARRIETT GREYSTONE   *Production Manager*

ISBN: 0-7172-8265-1
ISSN: 0273-1274

Stories on pages 16–27, 36–47, 56–67, 76–87, and all Disney character illustrations Copyright © 1992 by The Walt Disney Company

Illustration Credits and Acknowledgments

8–9—Artist, Michèle A. McLean; 10—(c) Gail Shumway; 11—(c) T. A. Wiewandt; 12—(c) Dwight R. Kuhn; 13—Belinda Wright/DRK Photo; 14–15—(c) Stephen Dalton/Photo Researchers, Inc.; 14—(c) Dwight R. Kuhn; 28—(c) Frank Zullo/Sipa Press; 29—(c) Dennis Oda/Sipa; 30–31—Autographed manuscript: The Granger Collection; 30—(c) Scala/Art Resource; 31—The Granger Collection; 32—(c) Lauros-Giraudon/Art Resource; 33—The Granger Collection; 34–35—Stamps courtesy Inter-Governmental Philatelic Corp.; 48—(c) Wilf Schurig/Animals Animals; (c) Stephen Dalton/Animals Animals; (c) Mike Bacon; 49—(c) Michael Habicht/Animals Animals; (c) Grant Heilman/Grant Heilman Photography; (c) Frans Lanting/Minden Pictures; 50—The Granger Collection; 51—North Wind Picture Archives; 52—(c) Giraudon/Art Resource; 53—North Wind Picture Archives; 54—The Granger Collection; 68—(c) Lane Stewart/*Sports Illustrated for Kids*; 69—(c) Andy Dappen; 70–71—(c) Lane Stewart/*Sports Illustrated for Kids*; 72—(c) Hal H. Harrison/Grant Heilman Photography; 73—Artist/Michèle A. McLean; 74—(c) C. Schmeiser/Unicorn Stock Photos; Jack Wilburn—Animals Animals/Earth Scenes; 75—(c) Jack Wilburn/Animals Animals/Earth Scenes; 88—(c) Bruno J. Zehnder/Peter Arnold, Inc.; 88–89—(c) Bruno J. Zehnder/Peter Arnold, Inc.; 89—(c) Steve Kaufman/Peter Arnold, Inc.; 90–91—(c) Michael George/Bruce Coleman, Inc.; 92—Gerry Ellis/Ellis Wildlife Collection; 93—(c) R. Norman Metheny/*Christian Science Monitor*; 94–95—Artist, Al Hering

Contents

You Are What You Eat — 6

Leapin' Lizards — 10

The Magic Coin — 16

A Sunsational Event — 28

Mozart—"The Little Magician" — 30

Disney Delivery — 34

Produce on the Loose — 36

Animal Face-Off — 48

Christopher Columbus's Voyage of Discovery — 50

Zillionaire for a Day — 56

Into the Woods! — 68

Who's Scared of Scarecrows? — 72

The Princess and the Genie — 76

A Winter Wonderland — 88

Pandas in Danger — 90

Say, What? — 94

YOU ARE
WHAT YOU EAT

Do you want to look and feel healthy? It's easy. Eat well-balanced, nutritious meals. What should you eat? Well, your body needs more than 50 different chemicals to be healthy. These chemicals are called nutrients. To make sure you're getting the nutrients you need, eat a variety of foods each day. Your diet should include the following:

Fruits and Vegetables. These give you carbohydrates (starches and sugars), your body's main source of energy. They also give you lots of vitamins A and C. And they contain fiber. Fiber helps move food and waste through the digestive system.

Bread and Cereal. These are made from grains. They contain fiber and are rich in B vitamins and iron. Whole-grain breads and cereals are best.

Milk, Cheese, and Yogurt. These are dairy foods, and they give you important vitamins. They're also rich in calcium, a mineral that's important when you're growing.

Meat, Poultry, Fish, Eggs, and Dried Beans and Peas. These are good sources of protein, which helps build new body tissues. Many of these foods also provide minerals, such as iron and zinc, and B vitamins.

Junk foods are high in sugar, fat, and salt. They aren't nutritious.

FOOD FOR THOUGHT

Sneaky Sugar

Foods that are high in sugar—like candy, cookies, and soda—aren't good for you. They have too many calories, which can sneak up on you and turn into fat. For a healthier snack, try an apple or an orange, or a glass of fruit juice.

Wonderful Water

Did you know that your brain is 75 percent water? Your blood has even more water—90 percent. Water is the single most important item in your diet. Your body could go for weeks without food. But it could only go a few days without water. So make sure to drink lots of water and other liquids, such as milk and juice.

Super Starch

Starchy foods like pasta, corn, beans, and baked potatoes have many nutrients and few calories. They provide the body with vitamins, minerals, and fiber, as well as energy. They should make up a big part of your diet. (Of course, you can't drown your pasta in rich sauce and your baked potato in sour cream!)

Tomato Tale

For years, people believed that tomatoes were poisonous. But in 1820, a man named Robert Johnson ate a whole basket of tomatoes in front of hundreds of people in Salem, New Jersey. They thought he had gone crazy—until they saw that he not only lived but didn't even get sick!

Breakfast Benefit

Do your parents insist that you eat a good breakfast before you go to school? They're right. Breakfast can help you feel better and perform better at school. But that doesn't mean that you should sit down to a heavy meal of bacon and eggs every morning. For a healthy breakfast, have fruit or juice, whole-grain cereal, and milk.

Fast Food Facts

More than 200 people order hamburgers every second! But about half the calories in burgers and most other fast foods come from fat. Try ordering healthier fast foods— burgers with lettuce and tomato instead of cheese, and low-fat frozen yogurt instead of ice cream.

LEAPIN' LIZARDS

Its bristly footpads let a gecko climb anywhere.

What sort of creature can climb a glass window? Walk upside-down across a ceiling? And bark like a dog? No, it's not some cross between Spiderman and Lassie. It's a tokay gecko, a lizard found in Asia. How can it climb on glass and walk across a ceiling? It has tiny bristles on its feet. These bristles are so fine that they can hook into the tiny pits that are on all surfaces—even glass. As for barking, the tokay gecko is in a class by itself. Most lizards don't make any sounds at all.

In addition to geckos, the lizard family includes chameleons, anoles, iguanas, gila monsters, and skinks. Altogether, there are about 3,000 different kinds of lizards. Most are less than 2 feet long. And some geckos are less than an inch in length. But the Komodo monitor lizard of Indonesia can range up to 10 feet in length. No wonder it's also known as the Komodo dragon!

Lizards are related to snakes. In fact, some lizards are legless and look just like snakes. But most lizards have legs, and they are used in different ways. One desert dweller, the fringe-toed lizard, has fringes on its toes. The fringes act like snowshoes, allowing the lizard to speed across the sand.

The fringe-toed lizard lives in the desert. The fringes on its toes act like little snowshoes, allowing the lizard to speed along the land.

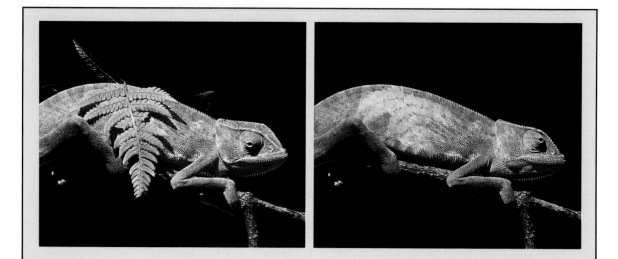

Quick=Change Artists

Long ago, the English poet Matthew Prior wrote this poem about the chameleon:

> *As the chameleon, who is known*
> *To have no colors of its own,*
> *But borrows from its neighbors hue*
> *His white or black or green or blue.*

As this poem indicates, chameleons are the masters of color changing. They can display a range of hues and even change the patterns on their skin. The lizards change color as a physical reaction to changing temperature and light conditions. Fright and anger also make them change color.

Some lizards—most chameleons, for example—live in trees. They have special tails that they use to grip branches. A group of Asian lizards called flying dragons also live in trees. They don't actually fly, though. Like flying squirrels, they glide from tree to tree by spreading out folds of skin along their sides.

To snakes, birds, and other kinds of animals, lizards are delicious meals. As a result, lizards have developed some interesting defenses. Some can grow lighter or darker in color to blend in with their surroundings. This camouflage helps them escape hungry animals. The Australian frilled lizard defends itself in a different way. It unfolds a large, collar-like frill around its neck, opens its mouth, and hisses. It looks very frightening. But such displays are usually bluffs. Most lizards aren't fighters.

Insects are the ideal meal for small lizards. Chameleons catch insects with their tongues. When the chameleon spots a tasty-looking bug, its tongue—which can be 5½ inches long—shoots out, unfolding like an accordion. The insect is caught on the tongue's sticky, forked tip and whipped back into the chameleon's

When threatened, the Australian frilled lizard unfolds the "collar" around its neck and hisses.

A chameleon catches a tasty-looking bug with its long, sticky tongue.

mouth. Some lizards also eat snails, crabs, and other small animals or bird eggs. Most large lizards eat plants. But Komodo dragons sometimes eat small wild pigs, goats, and even deer.

Chameleons use their excellent vision to catch insects. They can swivel their huge, bulging eyes in any direction. They can even look up or forward with one eye and down or back with the other—seeing two separate views at the same time. Geckos, which usually hunt at night, have large eyes that are designed to

The gecko's eyes are unusual because they have no eyelids. A gecko uses its tongue like a windshield wiper to clean its clear eye covering.

let in as much light as possible. This lizard doesn't have eyelids. Instead, its eyes are protected by a hard, clear covering.

Most lizards have good senses of taste and smell. Like snakes, many lizards use their tongues to pick up odors from the air or from objects that the tongue touches. Lizards also hear well. But except for the geckos, few make any sounds. Different geckos chirp, click, or, like the tokay gecko, bark. One type makes a loud call that sounds like "geck-o." This is how this lizard got its name.

Lizards are like their relatives, the snakes, in other ways, too. They hatch from eggs, and they're cold-blooded. This means that they can't keep their body temperature constant, as humans do, for example. They rely on their surroundings to supply warmth. So it's not surprising that most lizards live in warm areas. Wherever they live, lizards are in danger. They are hunted by other animals— and by people. And as people move into their wild areas, their natural homes are being destroyed. As a result, there are efforts today to protect some of these fascinating creatures.

The Magic Coin

Pinocchio the puppet was looking out the window of his father's wood-carving shop. The wishing star twinkled brightly in the sky. It was nearly time for Geppetto to come home for dinner. Soon all the wonderful clocks in Geppetto's shop would begin to tell the hour.

Pinocchio sighed.

"What's the matter, Pinoke?" asked his friend Jiminy Cricket.

"Oh, sometimes looking at all these wonderful clocks makes me sad," Pinocchio answered. "Geppetto has made so many clocks, but not one of them is mine. Not even the soldier clock," he said. "It's my favorite."

16

"Why don't you just ask Geppetto to give it to you?" suggested Jiminy. "I bet he would."

Pinocchio looked up at the wishing star. "I wish he would," he sighed.

As Pinocchio and Jiminy watched the star, it grew bigger and brighter. Soon the shop was filled with a blue light, and a beautiful lady dressed in blue appeared.

"It's the Blue Fairy!" gasped Jiminy.

The fairy bent over and touched Pinocchio's hand lightly with her magic wand. Then she spoke.

"I heard your wish, Pinocchio," she said, "and I'm going to grant it. Look in your hand."

Pinocchio opened his hand and found a gold coin. It twinkled in the blue light.

"That's a fairy coin," explained the fairy. "You can use it to buy something, or you can use it to wish for what you want. It will grant five wishes. You may use them all, or give some of them to someone else. But be careful. Good wishes are hard to make."

"Oh, I won't have any trouble," Pinocchio said.

"Just listen to Jiminy," she said. "He'll help you."

The fairy began to fade, and as she disappeared, she warned, "Be careful what you wish, Pinocchio."

Suddenly all the clocks began to tell the hour. On Pinocchio's favorite clock, which was shaped like a castle, a little drawbridge came down. Then out marched a group of toy soldiers. Each raised a tiny horn, tooted seven times, and marched back into the castle as the drawbridge closed behind them.

Pinocchio couldn't believe his good fortune. "First I'll wish for my favorite clock," he told Jiminy. He shut his eyes tightly and wished: "My first wish is to have the soldier clock!"

At that moment, Geppetto came in the door and gave Pinocchio a hug. "My boy," he said, "I've been thinking about something."

"What, Father?"

"You've been very good lately, and I want to reward you. You may have my soldier clock for your very own."

Pinocchio looked at Jiminy. "My first wish came true!" he
whispered.

That night, as Pinocchio was putting on his pajamas, Jiminy
asked him about his next wish.

"The second thing I'm going to wish for is a lot of money,"
Pinocchio said. "Then I can buy that sled I wanted, and a pair of
skates, and a pony to ride to school."

"Be careful about wishing for *things*," warned Jiminy. "Things
won't make you happy."

"Having my favorite clock makes me happy," Pinocchio pointed out. "A lot of money will make me happy, too."

The next morning Geppetto went out to deliver a clock and left Pinocchio in charge of the shop. The little puppet felt very important. He was sweeping the floor when a customer came in.

"Can I help you?" asked Pinocchio.

The man went straight to Pinocchio's soldier clock and took it off the wall. "I must have this clock," he said. "How much is it?"

"I'm sorry," said Pinocchio. "That clock isn't for sale."

"I'll pay you twice the price," said the man.

That was a lot of money. It would certainly buy the sled and skates Pinocchio wanted. But the soldier clock was his favorite, and Geppetto had given it to him.

"I'm sorry, sir," Pinocchio said firmly. "It's my very own clock. And it's not for sale."

"I'll give you five times the price," the man said. "I must have it!"

That was just too tempting for Pinocchio. Five times the price of the clock was a lot of money. Pinocchio thought about the sled and the skates again. And he thought about the pony he could ride to school.

"Sold," agreed Pinocchio sadly.

The man counted out the money and left, whistling happily and carrying Pinocchio's favorite clock.

When Geppetto came home, Pinocchio told him that he had sold the clock.

"I'm going to miss that clock so much, Father," said the little puppet unhappily.

"I'll miss it, too," sighed Geppetto.

"I wish I had it back!" said Pinocchio.

Then he realized that he had just made his third wish!

At that very moment, the man who had bought Pinocchio's clock came in.

"I must talk to the owner," he said.

"What's wrong?" asked Geppetto.

"I bought this clock today," the man said, "but when I got home, it wouldn't run."

"Would you like your money back?"

"Yes, please," said the man.

"That's no problem at all," said Geppetto. "We'll be quite happy to give you your money back. My son is very fond of this little clock."

When the man had gone, Geppetto sat down at his workbench to see if he could fix the soldier clock.

wanted. Then I didn't have the clock, but I had a lot of money. Now I have no money, but I do have a broken clock. And I've already used up three wishes."

Pinocchio took the magic coin out of his pocket and walked over to the window.

Pinocchio went quietly off to his room. He sat down on the bed, and Jiminy hopped up beside him.

"What's the matter, Pinoke?" asked Jiminy.

"Gosh, Jiminy," answered Pinocchio. "Wishing didn't turn out the way I thought it would. First I had the clock I had always

"What are you going to do?" asked Jiminy.

"I'm afraid to make any more wishes," Pinocchio answered. Then he tossed the coin out the window. It landed on the street below.

"I just wish my clock weren't broken," Pinocchio said to Jiminy as he sat back down on his bed.

Just then Geppetto called up the stairs to his son. "Pinocchio, your clock is working again," he said.

Pinocchio and Jiminy raced down the stairs. They got to the workshop just in time to watch the toy soldiers march out of the clock and toot their horns four times, for four o'clock.

Jiminy smiled. Pinocchio's fourth wish had come true, just as the Blue Fairy had promised. But what would become of the fifth wish?

Neither Jiminy nor Pinocchio saw the poor beggar woman who picked up the coin from the street.

"Oh, thank goodness!" she said. "I was wishing I could buy a warm coat for the winter. Now I can!" She didn't know that the coin she was holding was a wishing coin. She just knew that her wish, which was the fifth the coin could grant, had indeed come true.

The total solar eclipse on July 11, 1991, was a heavenly event.

A SUNSATIONAL EVENT

On July 11, 1991, a strange event took place during the day. The sun disappeared and people were left in the dark! It was a total solar eclipse. The moon passed between the sun and Earth, completely covering the sun and casting a dark shadow on Earth. The darkness lasted almost seven minutes in some places.

The path of the total eclipse started in the western Pacific Ocean and spread eastward to the island of Hawaii, southern Mexico, and parts of South America. A much larger area had a partial eclipse—only part of the sun was covered, and the sky darkened slightly.

What did the total eclipse look like? First, people saw the moon begin to pass in front of the sun. It appeared to take a round bite out of the edge of the sun. Soon the moon covered more and more of the sun. Just before the sun was totally covered, a circle of bright white light could be seen—the dark moon looked as if it were wearing a diamond ring. Then, when the sun was completely covered, there was another wondrous sight. People saw the solar corona—the brilliant outer atmosphere of the sun. It looked like a white halo around the moon. Also visible were flames of burning gases that shot outward from the sun's inner atmosphere.

The next total solar eclipse will be in 1992, over the southern Atlantic Ocean. Maybe you'll be lucky enough to see it.

Eclipse-Watching

You can watch an eclipse. But never look directly at the sun! *The sun's rays can damage your eyes and even cause blindness.*

The safest way to view an eclipse is through a pinhole viewer. Poke a pinhole in one side of a cardboard box. Opposite the pinhole, on the inside of the box, tape a sheet of white paper. Put the box over your head with the pinhole behind you. Face away from the sun. The sun's rays will pass through the pinhole and project an image of the eclipse onto the white paper.

Some people use blackened X-ray negatives to look at an eclipse. Whatever method you choose, be sure to talk with your parents or a teacher first.

MOZART
"THE LITTLE MAGICIAN"

His name was Wolfgang Amadeus Mozart. And he was a musical genius. He wrote the tune we know as "Twinkle Twinkle Little Star" at the age of 4. And he wrote his first symphony at the age of 8 and his first opera at the age of 12. Mozart grew up to become one of the world's greatest composers. When he died in 1791, he was only 35 years old. But he left behind hundreds of musical works. Many are still widely performed and loved today.

Wolfgang Amadeus Mozart as a boy (left) and as a man (right). He lived only 35 years, but in that time he gave the world some of its most loved music. Also shown is the house in Vienna, Austria, where Mozart wrote some of his famous works.

The 200th anniversary of his death was marked in 1991. Special performances of his works were held all around the world.

Mozart was born in Salzburg, Austria, on January 27, 1756. His father, Leopold, played the violin and composed music. When Wolfgang was only 3, he learned to pick out chords on the harpsichord, a piano-like instrument. His father then decided to give him music lessons. Young Mozart learned quickly. By the time he was 5, he was writing and playing minuets. Wolfgang's sister, Nannerl, was also a very talented musician. When Wolfgang was 6 and she was 11, they performed before the Empress of Austria.

The following year, the Mozarts began a three-year tour of Germany, France, England, and the Netherlands. Wolfgang played the harpsichord, the piano, the organ, and the violin. People called him "the little magician." It was during this tour that he wrote his first symphony—at the age of 8. And in 1768, at the age of 12, he wrote an opera called *La Finta Semplice* ("The Make-believe Simpleton").

In 1771, after a tour in Italy, Wolfgang and his father returned to Salzburg. Wolfgang was now 15. In the following years, his skill as a composer continued to grow. In 1781 he wrote the opera *Idomeneo*. Many consider this to be his first truly great opera.

At about the same time, Mozart moved to Vienna, the

Wolfgang, Leopold, and Nannerl at a Mozart family "jam session."

capital of Austria. There he married Constanze Weber, the daughter of a musical family. (The Mozarts had six children; only two sons survived.)

In Vienna, Mozart performed, taught, and composed. He wrote some of his greatest works, including the operas *The Marriage of Figaro* and *Don Giovanni*. In 1787 he was appointed to the Viennese court as a composer of chamber music.

In 1791, Mozart composed the comic opera *The Magic Flute*. It was one of his most famous works. And it was also one of his last. He died on December 5 of that year.

During his lifetime, Mozart wrote more than 800 works. Although he died young, his music seems likely to live on as long as there are people to play and listen to it.

Whiz Kids

A *"whiz kid"* is a young person who masters a difficult field. The word *"prodigy"* means exactly the same thing. Mozart was a prodigy. There have been many others. They usually appear in just a few fields —including math, chess, computer science, and music.

What makes a prodigy? First, the young person must have a special talent in one field. But talent isn't enough. He or she must have a family that is strongly supportive. And the prodigy must work very hard. But there should be time for other activities, too. Prodigies who are pushed too hard can fade in their teens or early 20's.

DISNEY DELIVERY

Have you ever heard of Antigua and Barbuda? The Gambia? Lesotho? Tanzania? What do they have to do with Donald Duck, Mickey Mouse, Bambi, and Goofy? Well, they are all small countries in the Caribbean and Africa. And they, like many other countries, have issued postage stamps that show Walt Disney's beloved cartoon characters.

Collecting stamps is fun. And one of the most exciting ways to collect stamps is to put together a topical collection. This kind of collection is made up of stamps on just one topic, or subject, such as

sports or animals or toys or flowers. Or Disney cartoon characters! There's even a Disney stamp album and a Disney stamp catalog for your collection. You might want to start out with a 1-cent Goofy, or a 10-cent Donald Duck, or an 85-cent Chip 'n Dale.

MICKEY THRU THE YEARS

He may not look it, but Mickey Mouse is middle-aged. In fact, he had his 60th birthday party in 1988. To help him celebrate, the Gambia issued a special group of nine stamps. These stamps show how Mickey has changed over the years. In the early years, for example, the Walt Disney artists painted Mickey by using regular paintbrushes. Today, they often use special air brushes. Also, Mickey's eyes have gone from solid black to having whites and pupils. Look carefully. What changes can you see in Mickey?

PRODUCE ON THE LOOSE

It was a typical case for Darkwing Duck. Vegetables were disappearing from St. Canard markets. The restaurants had no lettuce for their salads, and the markets had no tomatoes for their customers to make spaghetti sauce.

"Strange," said Darkwing, as he examined the produce section in the market where the latest theft had occurred. "The thief has only stolen vegetables. The fruits are all still here." He turned to his sidekick, Launchpad McQuack. "And didn't all these thefts occur at night?" he asked.

"Right, D.W.!" answered Launchpad. "Maybe the thief is a vegetarian who likes the dark."

Darkwing frowned. Launchpad had a talent for saying silly things.

The Terror That Flaps in the Night walked slowly down the aisle, looking into all the empty vegetable bins for clues.

Following his boss, Launchpad reached over and helped himself to a pear from a tall pile of fruit. But instead of a pear, Launchpad grabbed a cabbage that was hidden among the pears. He took a big bite.

"Yuck!" said Launchpad. "I didn't know that pears could taste like coleslaw!" He held up the cabbage and looked underneath it. "And I didn't know that pears had such long roots," he added.

"Pears don't have roots, Launchpad," snapped Darkwing. "They grow on trees. Now stop eating and look for clues."

"Sure, D.W.!" Launchpad tossed the cabbage away. But when it hit the floor, it got up and ran straight for the door, as fast as its roots could carry it.

Darkwing opened his bag of detective tools and pulled out his magnifying glass. He peered at the door and the floor.

"Hmmm . . ." he said. "No sign that anyone broke in, and no footprints. I'll have to use my amazing intelligence and prove, yet again, that I am the winged scourge that pecks at criminals' nightmares!"

"Uh . . . D.W." said Launchpad. "Do cabbages leave footprints? If they do, maybe we should follow the cabbage that just ran out of here."

But Darkwing wasn't listening. He was admiring himself in a glass door in the refrigerated section. He adjusted his hat and then turned away to continue his search for clues.

"There's not much here, Launchpad," he said after several minutes. "All I see in this section are fruits and nuts. Not a single vegetable."

"Yeah," Launchpad replied. "I guess that cabbage was just lost."

"Cabbage?" said Darkwing, startled. "What cabbage? I just told you there are no vegetables here. A cabbage is a vegetable."

"Well, whatever it is, it just went out the door."

Then Darkwing began to understand. Cabbages were walking out of buildings! Of course! Robot cabbages could only point to Dr. Reggie Bushroot, who loved plants so much that he had turned himself into one.

"Bushroot must be behind these vegetable thefts!" Darkwing said to Launchpad. "Follow that cabbage!"

As Darkwing was following the cabbage, his adopted daughter Gosalyn and her best friend Honker Muddlefoot were leaving for the dress rehearsal of their school play. Gosalyn and Honker were both playing killer cabbages.

Dressed in leafy green costumes, the two friends hurried toward the school auditorium. Just as they stepped into the crosswalk, THUNK! They crashed into an army of cabbages on a mission for Bushroot!

As Bushroot's cabbages picked themselves up and got back in line, Gosalyn and Honker got mixed in with them. They all ended up inside a produce market.

"What are we doing here?" whispered Honker to Gosalyn. "This doesn't look like the school auditorium."

Gosalyn looked around at all the other cabbages. "I thought *we* were the only killer cabbages in the play," she said.

Just then, the other cabbages pulled out spray guns and began to spray all the vegetables. Instantly, the vegetables grew root-legs and started walking out of the market!

"Honker, this must be how all the vegetables in St. Canard are disappearing!" cried Gosalyn. "Let's follow them!"

"But Gosalyn," said Honker, "shouldn't we tell your dad? This could be dangerous. Besides, we're late for the rehearsal."

"Come on, Honker," she said. "This could be our chance to be really big heroes. And maybe get some pointers on how real killer cabbages act!"

So the two fake cabbages filed out of the market with the real ones.

Meanwhile, Darkwing and Launchpad had followed their cabbage straight to Dr. Reggie Bushroot's greenhouse. They arrived just as Bushroot was arming another bunch of robot cabbages with spray guns.

"This is a dream come true," sighed Bushroot. "Soon I will have all the vegetables in St. Canard. Restaurants will have to come to me if their customers want salads. Markets will have to get their tomatoes from me."

Then he turned to his new cabbage troops. "Go to the Gander Street Market!" he ordered. "Bring me back all the vegetables you find!"

As Darkwing and Launchpad watched, the cabbages marched out of the greenhouse in single file.

Darkwing pulled his hat down securely on his head. "Let's get dangerous!" he hissed to his sidekick.

Darkwing leaped out of hiding and pulled his gas gun. "All right, Bushroot!" he shouted. "I've got you covered!"

"No, you don't!" Bushroot cried. "You're not going to ruin all my plans, Darkwing Duck!" He turned to a tree. "Get his gun!" he ordered.

But Darkwing quickly pulled out a lasso from under his coat. Using the rope, he grabbed his gun away from the tree.

Then Bushroot ordered a cranberry bush to shoot its red berries at Darkwing. As the masked crimefighter was dodging the splattering berries, in walked another crop of cabbages leading more vegetables.

"Not here!" Bushroot cried. "Go straight to the garden, so the new recruits can transplant themselves!"

But before the cabbages could change direction, Gosalyn and Honker threw off their leaves.

"Not you two brats, too!" cried Bushroot. Quickly he whistled for Spike, his Venus flytrap.

Meanwhile, Gosalyn had grabbed a fire extinguisher. She began to spray all the cabbages with cooling foam. One by one, the cabbages froze in their tracks.

"Gosalyn, what are you doing here?" shouted Darkwing, wiping red berry juice off his face.

"Honker and I got carried away by these cabbages on our way

to play rehearsal," Gosalyn explained. "Honker thought of the quick-freeze idea. Pretty neat, huh?"

"Well, freeze this!" shouted Reggie as he gave Spike the order to attack.

Quickly Gosalyn turned the fire extinguisher on Spike and sprayed. When the mist cleared, there were Spike and Reggie, frozen together!

"Gee, Gosalyn!" said Launchpad. "You got them both at once!"

"Good work!" said Darkwing. "I'm proud of you both. Now let's call the police, and we can all go home."

Gosalyn and Honker had missed their dress rehearsal. But the next night, after the school play, everyone agreed that their killer cabbages had given the most realistic performances of all!

What contests could these odd-looking animals win? The South American king vulture (*left*) gets the lumpiest-nose

award. The axolotl (*above*), a salamander, wins the alien-lookalike contest. The humpback wrasse (*right*) is named the funniest-looking clown.

With its 22 "nose rays," the star-nosed mole (*right*) is a shoo-in for the strangest-nose award. The male mandrill

(*above*), a kind of baboon, wins the most-colorful-face award. And when this male elephant seal (*left*) grows up, it will use its jumbo nose to win the seal-shouting contest.

Christopher Columbus reached the New World 500 years ago and claimed the land for Spain. That voyage changed the course of history.

Christopher Columbus's Voyage of Discovery

The year was 1492. From the Spanish port of Palos, three wooden ships sailed westward. They were commanded by the Italian navigator Christopher Columbus. Two months later, Columbus crossed the Atlantic Ocean and landed in the New World.

In 1992, millions of people on both sides of the Atlantic celebrated the 500th anniversary of that historic trip. Many people say that Columbus discovered America. But, even though

Europeans didn't know it, Indians had lived there for thousands of years. Because of Columbus's voyage, though, European colonies were started in the New World. This led to the founding of the America we know today.

Columbus was born about 1451 in the Italian port of Genoa. His father was a weaver, and he learned his father's trade. But Columbus became more interested in the sea. He made many voyages before traveling to Lisbon, Portugal, a center of trade and transportation. Many silk and spice traders were exploring sea routes to the East Indies, as Asia was then called.

In Portugal, Columbus made voyages for several traders. He also married, and he studied navigation. In the fifteenth century,

Columbus studied navigation. He thought he could sail west to Asia, instead of sailing around the southern tip of Africa.

Will the Real Christopher Columbus Please Stand Up

Christopher Columbus is one of the most famous people who ever lived—yet we don't even know what he looked like. There are more than seventy portraits of Columbus, including the one shown here. But not one was painted while he was alive.

There's even some mystery about his name. We call him Christopher Columbus, and the Spanish call him Cristóbal Colón. His son Ferdinand, who wrote a biography of Columbus, called him Colonus. But his real name at birth was probably Cristoforo Colombo.

people thought the world was very small. Columbus believed that he could find a shorter route to Asia—by sailing *west* around the globe. In 1484 he asked the king of Portugal to pay for a voyage to find the western route. The ruler turned him down, so in 1485 Columbus went to Spain. Queen Isabella, who ruled the country with her husband, King Ferdinand, was interested. But it took them until 1492 to decide to provide ships and crew for Columbus's voyage.

The expedition set sail on August 3, 1492. The three ships, the *Niña*, the *Pinta*, and the *Santa María*, were small, and

Columbus was brave to set out in them. But he thought the trip to Asia would be short—he had no idea that America lay in between. The ships stopped at the Canary Islands to pick up supplies. Then they sailed west for more than a month. Finally, in the early hours of October 12, land was sighted. The voyagers dropped anchor off one of the Bahama Islands. It was probably the island known today as San Salvador.

Columbus believed he had reached the East Indies, and so he called the island people "Indians." Columbus then sailed south. He hoped to find Cathay, as China was then called. But his ship was wrecked off the island of Hispaniola. He returned to Spain, where he was greeted as a hero.

Columbus's three ships were the Niña, *the* Pinta, *and the* Santa María. *He sailed on the* Santa María *(center), the largest of the three.*

Ferdinand and Isabella sent Columbus back to the New World the next year to found a settlement on Hispaniola. But Columbus was a poor governor. He was harsh with the Indians. The settlers constantly complained about life in the colony. And they complained about Columbus. All they were really interested in was gold. In 1500, Columbus was replaced as governor. He was stripped of his titles and sent to Spain to answer charges. Although his titles were later restored, he was never again allowed to govern in the New World.

In all, Columbus made four voyages to the New World. But he never found the passage to the East Indies. He returned to Spain

Columbus shows King Ferdinand and Queen Isabella jewelry, strange plants, and even several Indians from what he thought was Asia.

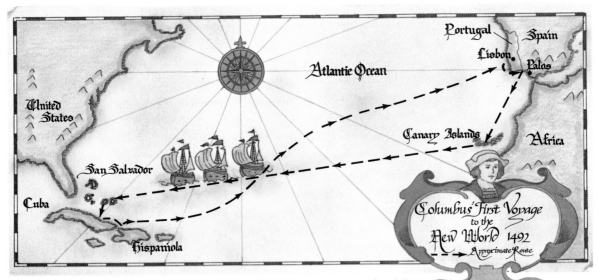

This map shows Columbus's first voyage to the New World. He made three other voyages, in 1493, 1498, and 1502.

for the final time in 1504. His last years were unhappy ones. He died on May 20, 1506, in Valladolid, Spain.

Many people believe that Phoenician, Roman, and Irish sailors reached the Western Hemisphere before Columbus. And there's evidence that Norsemen reached America around the year 1000. But Columbus was the explorer who was in the right place at the right time. His first voyage was made when Europeans were ready to explore and colonize distant lands.

Other explorers soon followed Columbus. And within a few years, Europeans realized the importance of the New World. Spain and Portugal, followed by the Netherlands, France, and England, began to colonize the Americas. There were some very sad chapters in this story. Indian civilizations were destroyed, and slavery was established in the colonies. But the outcome was the settlement and growth of the Western Hemisphere.

Zillionaire For A Day

"Nephew! Come in here!" called Scrooge McDuck, who was sitting in his office at his money bin.

"*Uh-oh!*" Donald Duck said to himself. "*I'm in trouble again.*" He jumped up from his desk and ran to his uncle's office.

"Stop!" said Scrooge as Donald entered. Scrooge straightened his glasses on his nose and looked carefully at his nephew.

"Yes," Scrooge finally said, "I think it will work."

"What will work?" asked Donald, afraid to move.

"I have a job for you," Scrooge answered. "This afternoon, I have to be at a very important business meeting. But I also have to be at City Hall with the mayor. He's giving me the Taxpayer of the Year Award, and I must be there to accept it."

"So?" Donald said. He wondered what this had to do with him.

"So *you're* going to pretend to be *me* at the mayor's office!" Scrooge replied.

"I'll never get away with it," said Donald.

"Nonsense!" Scrooge said. "With a little help, you'll look just like me."

Scrooge went to his closet and took out his extra coat, his extra hat, and his extra spats. Then he opened his desk drawer and took out some long pieces of hair and his extra pair of glasses.

"Look, Donald," he said. "If you wear my clothes and my glasses, and these false sideburns, no one will never know you aren't me."

Donald grumbled, but he put on Scrooge's clothes and glasses, and the fake sideburns. In a few minutes, Donald looked just like his uncle.

Scrooge was very pleased. "Perfect!" he said. "Now get going. My chauffeur is waiting for you—er, me—with the car."

So off Donald went. He climbed into the back seat of the fancy car. "To the mayor's office!" he ordered.

The driver didn't turn around, but he did say, "Yes, sir!" And the long, fancy car started away.

"*So far, so good*," Donald said to himself. He had even fooled Uncle Scrooge's own chauffeur!

As the big car rolled along, Donald was wishing that Daisy could see him wearing Scrooge's fancy coat and hat, and riding in Scrooge's fancy car. He turned his head to look out the window. Something was wrong! They were in an old, shabby part of town.

Donald tapped on the driver's shoulder. "This isn't the way to the mayor's office," he said.

Then the driver turned around and looked at the disguised duck. "There's been a little change in plans, Scroogie," he said with a mean smile.

Donald almost fainted. The driver was one of the terrible Beagle Boys!

"We didn't think you'd mind spending a few days as our guest," the Beagle Boy snickered.

The car's tires screeched as it turned into an alley and stopped in front of an old warehouse. Out of the building came two more Beagle Boys, and they pushed Donald inside.

"Welcome to our hideout, Scroogie!" said one.

"I'm not Scrooge!" wailed Donald.

"And we're not the Beagle Boys," said another Beagle Boy.

All three Beagle Boys laughed. "Yeah," said one. "We're the Three Musketeers! Haw! Haw! Haw!"

Then the Beagle Boy who had driven the car sat down at a table and began to write. When he had finished, he read the note to his brothers.

"*Dear Money Bin Guards,*" the note read. "*If you want to get Scrooge McDuck back, send all the money in the money bin to the old warehouse on Quacker Street. Yours truly, the Beagle Boys.*"

The other two Beagle Boys agreed that the ransom note was perfect. So the first Beagle Boy got back in the car. "You guys entertain our guest," he said. "I'll deliver the note."

When the money bin guards saw the terrible Beagle Boy get out of Scrooge's car, they reached for their guns.

"Relax, boys," said the Beagle Boy. "Read this." And he handed the note to the chief money bin guard.

When the guard had read the note, he was suspicious. "How do we know you really have Mr. McDuck?" he asked.

"That's his car," the Beagle Boy answered. "If we have his car, we have him!"

The guard had to agree. So he sent for Scrooge's fleet of armored trucks and had the other guards load all the money into them. It took 37 trucks.

While the guards were loading up Scrooge's zillion dollars, the Beagle Boy drove back to his hideout. He had never had a zillion dollars before, and he wanted to watch it arrive.

As soon as all the trucks were loaded, the chief guard read the

crumpled up the note, dropped it on the ground, and climbed into one of the trucks.

Meanwhile, the real Scrooge McDuck had finished his business meeting. He felt very good, because he had made a deal that would add a million dollars to the zillion he already had.

"I think I can take the afternoon off," he said to himself as he walked back to his money bin. "I'll take a swim in my money."

But when Scrooge got to his money bin, there was no money for him to swim in. All he found was a big, empty room. He ran back outside to look for the guards. But he couldn't find any of them, either. What could have happened?

Then Scrooge saw the crumpled note on the ground. He picked it up, smoothed it out, and read it.

"Oh, no! The terrible Beagle Boys!" he groaned. "They must have Donald, and they think he's me! And my guards have taken them all of my money . . . just to get Donald back!" The thought brought tears to his eyes.

Then Scrooge got hold of himself. He ran back into his empty money bin, picked up the telephone, and began to dial.

Meanwhile, back at the Beagle Boys' hideout, the armored trucks had begun to arrive. One by one, they dumped loads of money in front of the warehouse. The Beagle Boys couldn't believe their eyes. One of their plans was finally working!

"A zillion dollars!" one of them exclaimed.

"How do we know it's really a zillion?" said another, scratching his head. "None of us can count over ten."

The third Beagle Boy wasn't listening. He had jumped into the

mountain of money. He was playing in it as if it were a pile of leaves. "Yippee!" he shouted. "We're zillionaires!"

The Beagle Boys were so excited that none of them heard the sirens that were getting closer and closer.

Soon the hideout was surrounded by police cars. Out of one police car jumped Scrooge, yelling, "Get out of my money!"

Well, those terrible Beagle Boys were very disappointed. The person they had tied to a chair in their hideout wasn't Scrooge McDuck at all. He was just Donald Duck, and he was only worth about fifty cents a day (which is what Scrooge paid him), not a zillion dollars.

So the Beagle Boys went back to jail, and Scrooge's zillion dollars was rescued. Scrooge was about to follow his money back to his money bin when he remembered: He was supposed to rescue his nephew, too!

Scrooge found Donald and untied him. As the two Scrooges walked toward Scrooge's big, fancy car, Donald apologized. "I'm sorry I didn't get your award for you, Uncle Scrooge," he said.

"That's all right, nephew," Scrooge answered. "I just realized something. The award ceremony is tomorrow. I got my dates mixed up."

And then he added, "But this time, I think I'll go *myself!*"

INTO THE WOODS!

"There is pleasure in the pathless woods." The English poet Lord Byron wrote this line almost two hundred years ago. Today, more and more people are learning how right he was.

People have always enjoyed hiking or camping in the woods. And now there's a new group of woods-lovers. These people are called "orienteers," or "O-ers." The name comes from the word "orient," which means to find your bearings. Or put another way, it means to know where you are in the woods, and to be able to get from where you are to where you want to go.

Many O-ers do this as a sport. They race each other through woodland areas. They don't have to follow the same route—but they must all reach certain landmarks. To participate, O-ers need only a compass and a map. O-ers' maps are called O-maps. These are special maps that show lakes, streams, rivers, ponds, and swamps. They show wooded areas and clearings. And they show hills and valleys, trails and roads. There are also lines on the map that show where the land is level and where it slopes up or down.

But you don't have to be a racer to enjoy orienteering. Lots of people do it just for the fun of being outdoors and testing their map skills. There are a number of orienteering clubs that have woodland courses for people of all ages and abilities.

Orienteers try to reach a series of landmarks, or control points. To do this, they must use a special map and compass. The control points are usually shown by orange and white markers.

Be Prepared!

If you go orienteering, you must be prepared. There are three important things you should always have:
- *O-map. These special maps are extremely detailed and accurate.*
- *Compass. Many O-ers use a baseplate compass. The needle rests in a clear plastic baseplate. This makes it easy to set a course from where you are to where you want to go.*
- *Proper Clothing. Wear loose, comfortable clothing and hiking boots. Shorts won't give you enough protection. And carry a whistle. If you have a problem, you can signal for help.*

Here's how orienteering works: You must go through the woods and reach a series of landmarks, called control points. How you get to each one depends on how well you can read the map and use the compass. The landmarks are shown on the map—but they aren't easy to find. When you do reach a landmark, there's usually an orange and white marker identifying it.

What would you do in a situation like this? You look at your map and see that the next landmark is beneath a ridge,

about half a mile to the east. The route straight to the ridge looks like flat ground. But wait! The map also shows that there are some wetlands there. Maybe it's a swamp filled with mosquitoes. You say to yourself, "If I follow the shorter route and go straight ahead, will I have to slosh through a lot of muck? Would it be better to go around the wetlands?" You have to decide. You think, "It hasn't rained lately. Maybe the wetlands have dried out a little." So off you go toward the swamp. As you make your way, you're watching for your landmark, the ridge.

Meanwhile, some other orienteer has chosen the high ground. She's going toward the ridge by circling to the north. It's a longer route, but there's little chance of getting bogged down with a bunch of frogs.

Which route would *you* have chosen?

Whichever one it was, you would have had the pleasure of experiencing nature in a wonderful way—finding your way through the wilderness on foot.

Who's Scared of Scarecrows?

In *The Wizard of Oz*, Dorothy and her dog, Toto, meet the Tin Woodman, the Cowardly Lion, and the Scarecrow. They find the Wizard and ask him to grant them their wishes. The Tin Woodman wants a heart. The Cowardly Lion wants to be brave. And the Scarecrow? He wants brains inside his head instead of stuffing.

But it isn't only the heads of scarecrows that are stuffed—they're usually stuffed all over. Scarecrows are made out of old clothes that are filled with straw or rags. They're mounted on sticks and placed in fields to frighten away crows and other animals that eat crops and seeds. Scarecrows have been used by farmers in just about every country of the world to scare away pests. The farmers hoped that the figures would look like real people to the hungry animals.

Scarecrows were very popular in Europe during the Middle Ages. And when European colonists came to the New World in the early 1600's, they made scarecrows that were just like those that had been made in Europe. They stuffed old clothing with hay, leaves, grass, or straw and

Build Your Own Scarecrow

To build a scarecrow, you'll need old clothes, stuffing material (rags, straw, or leaves), a bucket or a plastic pumpkin for the head, and one long and one short stick.

1. Nail or tie the two sticks together to form a cross.
2. Slip the longer stick through one pants leg. Let the other leg hang free.
3. Put a shirt or jacket on the shorter stick.
4. Stuff the pants and shirt.
5. Put the head on top of the longer stick.
6. Dig a deep hole in the ground and stand the scarecrow in it. Pack the dirt down.

Do scarecrows really frighten birds away? Probably not. Bird experts say that loud noises and movement are what frighten the birds. That's why loudspeakers, firecrackers, and other devices are now used to scare the birds.

topped the head with a straw hat. Sometimes a farmer would find that the old clothes had mysteriously disappeared during the night—a poor tramp may have liked the scarecrow's garments better than his own.

held in the fall, and prizes are awarded for the most original designs. Some recent favorites at the shows have been scarecrows that looked like gremlins, Cabbage Patch dolls, witches, and dragons. One even looked like Bart Simpson!

But people are still building scarecrows today. In fact, many people fancy themselves as "scarecrow sculptors." They take part in the scarecrow contests that are held in towns across the United States. These contests are usually

The Princess and the Genie

Once upon a time, there was a princess named Roberta. She had everything a princess could want, except a friend to keep her company. No matter how many royal books she read, or how many royal lessons she had in singing and dancing, she was royally bored!

One afternoon the Princess was gazing out her window, wishing she were down on the beach building a sand castle. Suddenly she spied a big, shiny bottle in the waves.

"I wonder what's in that bottle," she said to herself. She pulled off her crown and tossed it on the bed. Then she ran down the stairs and out the back door of the castle.

Princess Roberta pulled the bottle out of the water. It was very heavy, and by the time she had dragged it up onto the dry sand, she was as wet and sandy as it was.

The bottle was the color of very old gold. It had strange carvings all over it, and a big brass stopper in the top.

"What a funny-looking bottle!" the Princess said. "I think I had better open it right away."

So Princess Roberta pulled out the stopper. A cloud of green

smoke flowed out of the bottle. Then it began to rock back and forth, making weird, grunting noises.

Suddenly there was a loud POP! A head, two arms, and a body with a saggy bottom poked out of the bottle. Then came two long, skinny legs and, finally, two big feet.

To Roberta's surprise, what was in the funny-looking bottle was a very funny-looking genie.

"Gawrsh!" said the genie, stretching his arms and legs. "I don't think I'll ever get the hang of gettin' out of bottles." Then he noticed the Princess.

"Thanks for lettin' me out," said the genie. "Pleased to meet you. I'm Goofus. I'm a student genie."

"I'm Princess Roberta," the Princess answered. "How did you get into that bottle?"

"My teacher put me in," Goofus explained. "I failed Wish Granting class sixteen times, so he put me in this bottle. I only have one more chance to make three wishes come true. If I can't do it, I'm bottled for good!"

"How awful!" the Princess cried.

"You're tellin' me!" sighed the
genie. "It's real uncomfortable
in there!"

He pulled a book out of his pocket and flipped through the
pages. "Let's see . . . it says here that the person who lets a
genie out of a bottle gets to make three wishes." He looked at the
Princess. "I need to grant three wishes, so I guess it's up to you."

Princess Roberta looked stumped.

"Tell me what you want, Princess," Goofus suggested. "Take
your time and think of somethin' good. But make it kind of easy."

The Princess tried, but she couldn't think of even one wish. "How about jewels and gold?" Goofus said.

The Princess shook her head. "I have all that stuff already," she said. "It just sits in my jewelry box all day. It's boring."

"Well, how about a great big house?" Goofus suggested. "With ninety-nine bathrooms, and three hundred bedrooms, and . . ."

The Princess interrupted him. "Oh, no," she said. "What would I do with all those empty rooms? Besides, I already live in a castle. It's boring, too."

Goofus was beginning to look worried, and the Princess felt sorry for him. But she just couldn't think of a wish to make.

Then the genie's stomach growled.

" 'Scuse me!" Goofus blushed. "I haven't eaten in about three hundred years, and I'm kind of hungry."

"That's it!" cried Roberta. "I'll wish for something to eat!"

"Great!" Goofus said. So he stood on his head, bent one leg over his right ear, shut his eyes, and began to chant. "Gimmedy, gottame, have-a-me-good! Make-um come-um a lottum food!" He opened his eyes. No food had appeared.

"Gawrsh, I was sure I could grant that little wish," he sighed.

Just then a sausage-seller came by with hot sausages.

"Say, those look good!" said Goofus. He ran up to the sausage-seller and traded a jewel from the back of his cap for two fat, juicy sausages wrapped in soft, flaky rolls. Soon he and Princess Roberta were having a picnic.

"Oh, Goofus!" Princess Roberta cried as she daintily ate her food. "Do you realize you just made my first wish come true?"

"I did!" said the genie, smiling. "Think of another one fast, before I lose my touch!"

Roberta thought again, but she still couldn't think of a wish.

"How about a trip around the world?" Goofus said.

"I've been everywhere at least three times," the Princess sighed. "I was all by myself, and it was pretty boring."

Goofus hung his head. He didn't know what else to suggest.

"Wait a minute!" cried Roberta. "There is one place. I've never been to the village." Then she remembered why. "But if I went there, everyone would know who I am. My mom and dad, the King and Queen, would find out, and I'd get in trouble."

"You could go if you were invisible," Goofus said, perking up.

"Good idea," said the Princess. "I wish I were invisible!"

Goofus jumped to his feet. He spun around twenty-nine times and jumped up and down thirteen times. He put his fingers in his

ears, closed his eyes, and yelled, "Lookaway, snookaway, blinkum eyes!"

But when he opened his eyes, there was the Princess.

"I guess my wish didn't work," sighed Roberta.

Just then, Goofus saw a peasant girl playing on the beach. "I've got a great idea," he said. He went up to the girl and traded two

jewels from his cap for her tattered shawl. Then he draped the shawl over the Princess's head and shoulders.

"No one will recognize me like this," laughed the Princess. "It's as good as being invisible. You've granted my second wish!"

The two raced into the village, where they saw people working and people playing. They bought cookies and chestnuts to eat.

They played a game with the village children after school.

As they were strolling back to the beach, Roberta said, "I had a wonderful time, Goofus. I wasn't bored once!"

"And I've granted two whole wishes!" Goofus said proudly. "Think of one more, and I'll be free."

The Princess thought as hard as she could, but she still couldn't think of anything else to wish. "Phooey!" she said. "I can't do it, and now it's time for me to go home."

"Please!" begged Goofus. "Just one more wish!"

"I wish I could," said Roberta. "I really want to help you. I've had more fun today than I had all last year. I wish I had a friend like you!"

"You've done it!" cried Goofus. "I don't need a magic spell to

make that wish come true!" He grabbed the Princess's hands and they danced around the bottle. "I'll be your friend forever!"

Suddenly lightning flashed, and a loud voice called down from the sky. "Goofus," the voice said, "you are free forever!"

The Princess and the genie were so surprised they couldn't speak. Then they started to laugh.

"Come on, friend," said Roberta. "Let's go home."

So Goofus went to live in the castle. Every Monday, he and Roberta sneaked into the village and played with the village

children after school. On the other days, they shared other wonderful adventures. Goofus took his lessons with the Princess, and he proved to be very good at un-genie-like things like arithmetic and spelling.

And Princess Roberta was never, ever bored again!

A WINTER WONDERLAND

Do you live where the winters are cold? If you do, then you've probably tried to make snow sculptures. Perhaps it was a simple snowman. Or maybe you and your friends built a snow house. Working with snow can be a lot of fun. That's why snow sculpture contests have become popular events in many areas.

One of the largest snow sculpture events is held on Hokkaido, Japan's northernmost island. It's called the Sapporo Snow Festival. It began in the early 1950's, when some high-school students decided to build snowmen in the city park.

Today, many of the sculptures are palaces, castles, animals, and snow slides. Others are TV or cartoon characters. They fill an area eleven blocks long. The sculptors use axes, saws, spades, chisels, and other tools to carve their beautiful figures from snow and ice.

After the festival ends,

bulldozers knock the sculptures down. If they were left to melt, the huge sculptures might fall and hurt someone. All that's left of the artists' works are memories and photographs like the ones shown here.

PANDAS IN DANGER

They look like big stuffed animals. They're playful and good natured, and their antics make us laugh. They are giant pandas, and they're among the most loved animals in the world. All the wild giant pandas live in bamboo forests in the mountains of central China. But today there are fewer than a thousand of them in the wild, and there are only about a hundred in zoos. These wonderful animals are in danger! How did this happen?

The giant panda is a roly-poly, black-and-white creature with a large round head and a short tail. It's especially known for the

PANDA-MONIUM

- *The giant panda's closest relative is the bear. The Chinese call the panda "daxiong mao," which means "large cat bear."*
- *When it eats, a panda sits on its haunches—just the way a human being does.*
- *To get enough nutrition, a panda spends about 16 hours a day eating bamboo. It may eat as much as 5 tons of bamboo in one year.*
- *Pandas make many different sounds. They moo and moan, whine and snort, bleat and chirp, growl, squeak, bark, and roar.*

large black patches around its eyes, which give the animal such a lovable look. Pandas are about 5 feet long and weigh more than 200 pounds. They love to frolic and have been seen doing somersaults and belly-flops down snowy slopes. Sometimes they swim and climb trees. And in zoos, they play with rubber balls and other toys. Yet they spend most of their time alone, not with other pandas. They usually get together only during the mating season in spring.

Pandas give birth a total of four or five times in a lifetime, but only two cubs will make it to adulthood. Even fewer pandas cubs in zoos reach adulthood. The fact that so few pandas reach adulthood is one reason for their declining numbers.

Another reason is their diet. The panda's basic food is bamboo. Bamboo is a woody grass that grows as tall as trees. It isn't a very nutritious food, so pandas must eat lots of it. At one time, bamboo was plentiful in China. But over the years, the bamboo forests have been cut down to make way for farms, villages, and roads. This is destroying the pandas' main source of food.

Despite these problems, poaching (illegal hunting) is the major reason for the decline of the giant panda. The magnificent panda pelts sell for lots of money, and poachers kill pandas in great numbers to get the pelts.

All the wild giant pandas live in China. Their main food is bamboo. But many of China's bamboo forests have been destroyed.

Killing pandas is against the law in China. Here, a policemen's chalkboard is used to tell people about the punishment of poachers.

The Chinese government, wildlife organizations, and zoos around the world are taking steps to prevent the giant panda from becoming extinct. Starting in the 1960's, the Chinese government began to set up a number of reserves for the pandas, to protect the animals and their bamboo forests. Even more reserves are going to be set aside in the next few years. The government and a number of zoos are also trying to find ways to improve the breeding of pandas in captivity. And, most important, the Chinese government is handing out harsh sentences to anyone found panda poaching.

People everywhere hope that these efforts will allow the endearing, cuddly giant panda to survive.

Say, What?

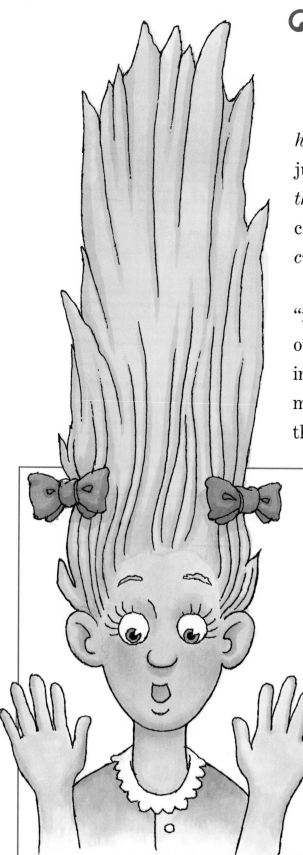

I told a friend about my *hair-raising experience*. But it just went *in one ear and out the other*. I was so angry I could have cried—and not *crocodile tears*, either!

These expressions are called "idioms." And you can't figure out their meanings from the individual words in them. You must know the stories behind the idioms to understand them.

A Hair-Raising Experience

Have you ever been scared and felt the hair on your head and body stand up? This often happens to people. And it happens because of something called the pilomotor reaction. It's one of the ways in which our bodies react to fear— nerve endings under the skin cause our hair to stand up. A hair-raising experience, then, is a frightening one.

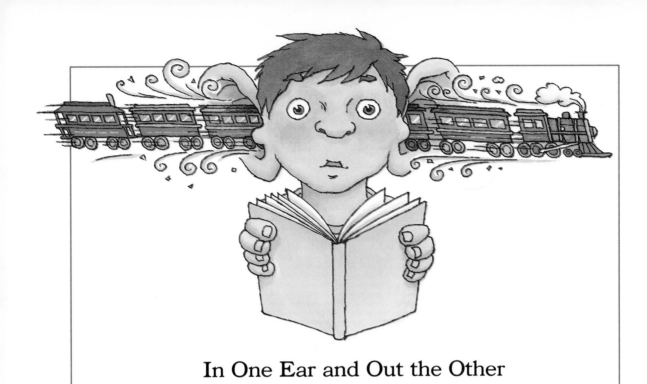

In One Ear and Out the Other

"In one ear and out the other" means to hear something without really paying attention to it. It's as if someone speaks to you and their words enter your head through one ear and pass right through, without being captured by your mind.

Crocodile Tears

Do crocodiles cry? No. But long ago, someone made up a tall tale. The tale said that hungry crocodiles lured people by making sobbing noises. Then they shed tears as they ate the people up. This story led to the idiom "crocodile tears." They are tears shed by people who make believe they feel sorry but really don't.